To the reader:

D1485077

Welcome to the DK ELT Graded Reade
different. They explore aspects of the world around us. Its
history, geography, science … and a lot of other things. And
they show the different ways in which people live now, and
lived in the past.

These DK ELT Graded Readers give you material for
reading for information, and reading for pleasure. You are using
your English to do something real. The illustrations will help
you understand the text, and also help bring the Reader to life.
There is a glossary to help you understand the special words for
this topic. Listen to the cassette or CD as well, and you can
really enter the world of the Olympic Games, the *Titanic*, or
the Trojan War … and a lot more. Choose the topics that
interest you, improve your English, and learn something …
all at the same time.
Enjoy the series!

To the teacher:

This series provides varied reading practice at five levels of
language difficulty, from elementary to FCE level:
Beginner
Elementary A
Elementary B
Intermediate
Upper Intermediate
The language syllabus has been designed to suit the factual
nature of the series, and includes a wider vocabulary range than
is usual with ELT readers: language linked with the
specific theme of each book is included and
glossed. The language scheme, and ideas
for exploiting the material
(including the recorded
material) both in and out of
class are contained in the
Teacher's Resource Book.
We hope you and your
students enjoy using this series.

WITHDRAWN FROM STOCK

Treloar College
R05128P2386

A DORLING KINDERSLEY BOOK

[DK] www.dk.com

Originally published as Eyewitness Reader
Shark Attack! in 1998 and adapted as an
ELT Graded Reader for
Dorling Kindersley by

studio cactus ●

13 SOUTHGATE STREET WINCHESTER HAMPSHIRE SO23 9DZ

Published in Great Britain by
Dorling Kindersley Limited
9 Henrietta Street, London WC2E 8PS

2 4 6 8 10 9 7 5 3 1

Copyright © 2000
Dorling Kindersley Limited, London

All rights reserved. No part of this publication
may be reproduced, stored in a retrieval system,
or transmitted in any form or by any means,
electronic, mechanical, photocopying, recording,
or otherwise, without the prior written permission
of the copyright owner.

A CIP catalogue record for this book is
available from the British Library.

ISBN 0-7513-3177-5

Colour reproduction by Colourscan, Singapore
Printed and bound in China
by L. Rex Printing Co., Ltd
Text film output by Ocean Colour, UK

The publisher would like to thank the following for their
kind permission to reproduce their photographs:
a=above; c=centre; b=below/bottom; l=left; r=right; t=top

Ardea London: Kev Deacon 11 b, 13; P. Morris 7;
D. Parer & E. Parer-Cook 19 tl; Ron & Valerie Taylor 11 c,
12, 15 cl, 18, 19 tr, 25 t, 28 b, 29 cl, br, 30 t, cl, 37 br, 38 c,
40 tr; Adrian Warren 19 b; **Bruce Coleman Ltd**: Michael
Glover 37 tr; **Mary Evans Picture Library**: 14 br; **The
Ronald Grant Archive**: *Jaws: The Revenge*, 1987 ©
MCA/Universal Pictures 14 bl; **T. Britt Griswold**: 38 bl;
Innerspace Visions: Kurt Amsler 41 b; Bob Cranston 25 b;
Nigel Marsh 40 bl; Doug Perrine 46 t; **Oxford Scientific
films**: Richard Herrmann 37 cl; **Pictor International**: 41 tr;
Planet Earth Pictures: F. J. Jackson 27; Doug Perrine 15 b, 28
t, 42 cl; Marty Snyderman 10; James D. Watt 38–39, 47;
Norbert Wu 15 cr; **Science Photo Library**: BSIP LECA 44;
Eye of Science 35; **Smithsonian Institution, NMNH**: Chip
Clark 33 outer; **Waterhouse stock Photography**: Stephen
Frink 45; **Wild Images**: Howard Hall 31.
Jacket credit: **Telegraph Colour Library**: front cover main.

Contents

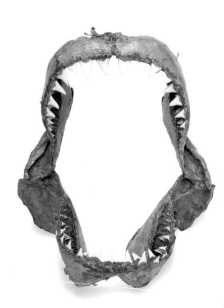

ELT Graded Readers

ELEMENTARY B

SHARK!

Written by

Sarah Woolard

Series Editor Susan Holden

London • New York • Delhi • Sydney

Shark Attack!

"I must find a big fish – and soon!" thought Rodney, and he looked around in the water. Rodney was a young Australian fisherman, and he really loved fishing underwater. Now he was in an important fishing competition. To win the competition, he had to catch the biggest fish with his spear gun. Last year, Rodney won the competition – he was the best fisherman in the area, the champion! This year, he wanted to win again, but he was worried – he didn't have many fish. Rodney was looking for a really big fish, but luckily, he didn't know what was going to happen next!

All the fishermen in the competition wore special diving equipment – a diving suit, a mask, and a diving belt with a long line (*see the picture on page 5*). Each fisherman carried a spear gun to kill the fish. Every time they caught a fish, they put it on their line. Later, they could see who had the most – and the biggest – fish.

There was one prize for the fisherman who caught the most fish, and another prize for the fisherman who caught the biggest fish. The person with the biggest fish was the champion, and the person with most fish was the "runner up". Sometimes the same person won both prizes. Rodney really wanted to win.

Shark capital
Most shark attacks in the world are in Australia. It is the shark attack capital of the world. But there are not many attacks – less than 300 in the past 100 years.

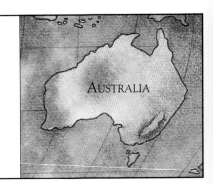

AUSTRALIA

After two or three hours, the fishermen had a lot of fish on their lines. It was noisy and smelly – you could smell the blood from the dead fish in the water. Rodney was still looking around, he was thinking about the competition. "I need to catch more fish to win this competition," he said to himself.

Suddenly, he saw a big fish about one kilometre away. "It's a morowong!" he thought. "If I catch this fish, I can win the competition. A morowong is a really big fish! I'll be the champion again!" Carefully, he turned around and pointed his spear gun at the fish. But Rodney didn't catch the morowong – he didn't have time.

CRASH! "What was that?!" he thought. Something hit Rodney hard on his side. It felt like a fast train! "That's not a morowong!" thought Rodney. "Morowongs are big … but this is huge!" He thought again. "Oh no! Perhaps it's a shark!" Rodney felt very frightened. He looked around to see what had hit him.

It was a great white shark! When the shark crashed into Rodney, his mask fell off his face, and his spear gun fell out of his hand. A few seconds later, Rodney's shoulder was inside the shark's mouth! With its sharp teeth, the huge shark bit into his chest and back. Rodney was terrified – he pushed and turned, trying to get away. But he had no gun, and he had no mask. How was he going to escape?

He hit the shark with his hand, but the shark did not open its mouth. It held him in its teeth and moved him from side to side to kill him. What could Rodney do? It was impossible – the shark was too strong, and he was getting tired. He was feeling very afraid.

Then suddenly he remembered something – he knew the weak point on a shark!

"I must try to hit its eye – the shark's weakest point," thought Rodney.

Rodney pulled his arm back and hit the shark's eye very hard with his hand. It worked! The shark opened its mouth and Rodney fell out. He was free! He felt very surprised. Sharks do not usually open their mouths! They usually wait until the person is dead.

Rodney was very, very lucky. But he knew that he didn't have much time. He had to get out of the water as soon as possible to survive.

Shark's eyes
How does a shark protect its eyes?
A shark can move its eyes back into its head when it is attacked. Some sharks have a special cover they can pull down over their eyes when there is danger.

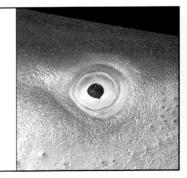

He decided to swim up to the surface as quickly as possible.
But Rodney was not out of danger. He was bleeding, he was
weak and frightened – and he didn't have much air. He had
to get out of there quickly and get help. He tried to swim up
to the surface to get his head out of the water. But where was
the shark? Could he get away before the great white shark
came back and ate him alive?

SPLASH! Rodney's head was out of the water and he breathed in the air.

"I'm OK!" he thought, and he started to feel safe. But then he looked down. "Oh no!" The shark was coming straight for him – fast! Its huge jaws were wide open, and you could see its sharp teeth – all of them!

"Not again!" thought Rodney, terrified. "What can I do now?" He felt weak again.

SNAP! The shark's teeth closed again – but where was it? This time it didn't bite Rodney, it took one of the fish on his line. But the line was still on Rodney's diving belt! Suddenly he was moving – the shark was pulling him through the water again on the end of the diving belt. He was like one of the dead fish on the line!

The shark dived down and down into the sea, pulling the line and Rodney behind it. Rodney didn't know what to do this time – he didn't have a knife to cut the line, and he was still bleeding a lot. "I must take off my belt," he thought.

Quickly, he tried to take off his belt, but he was weak and he was moving too fast, and it was difficult to see or do anything. It was no good – he couldn't open it.

There was no time to think now. He knew he was in serious danger. He was going to die! "Will the shark eat me, or will I drown?" he asked himself. His head was aching and his shoulder was hurting. He was feeling weaker and weaker.

Suddenly the line broke. Rodney was free! He didn't have time to think. He swam up to the surface again and shouted for help.

Luckily, some friends were near in their fishing boat, and they heard him shouting and splashing in the water. They quickly pulled him out of the water and into their boat.

"What happened?" asked one of his friends. But Rodney couldn't say anything. Then they saw his diving suit – they could see where the shark's teeth went through his suit and into his body – and they knew that it was serious. Rodney needed help quickly. The top part of his body was cut open, and it was difficult for him to breathe.

His friends looked at him, and then at one another. "There is not much time – he needs a doctor now," they said quietly. Luckily, fishermen understand danger. They know how to save lives. They know that it is important to find help quickly. They always help each other when there is a problem – next time, they could be in danger. You need friends when you are a fisherman!

After a great white shark bite, most people die. But not Rodney Fox – he was lucky – he lived!

Quickly, Rodney's friends got help, and took Rodney to the nearest hospital. The doctors at the hospital operated on him for four hours. When the doctors closed up the hole in Rodney's body again, they gave him 462 stitches. "You're going to have an ugly scar on your body for the rest of your life," the doctors told him.

Rodney smiled and said, "But I am alive! I am lucky."

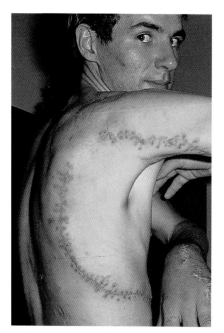

The story of Rodney Fox and the shark attack was on television and in all the newspapers – it was big news. When they heard about it, many people were frightened to go to the beaches and into the water. They asked the government to keep the sharks away from the beaches. But they wanted to kill the sharks, and Rodney didn't agree with this. Many fishermen respect sharks. They are dangerous, but the fishermen understand them.

Dangerous teeth
A shark's mouth can have six rows of teeth. Each tooth is very sharp and like a triangle. When one tooth falls out, another grows in. A great white shark can have 100 teeth.

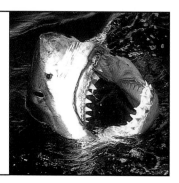

Rodney didn't want to go out and kill sharks, he wanted to learn more about them. He thought they were very strange and interesting, and so he started to study them. It was now the most important thing for him – he loved sharks, and for the rest of his life he wanted to learn about these silent killers of the sea.

Everyone was surprised. "A shark tried to kill you!" said his friends. "You can still see the scar on your body! How can you do this?" Rodney couldn't explain his new love, but he didn't stop.

A few months after the attack, Rodney was swimming in the sea again. He wanted to get near the sharks – but he didn't want to die. How could he do this? Rodney thought about the problem, and then he had an idea. He made a special box to put in the water – big enough to stand inside. It was the first shark cage. With the shark cage, he could be near the sharks, but they couldn't attack him.

Rodney Fox now dives with sharks, and is trying to help them.

So what is a shark cage? It is a small box to protect people under the water when they are watching and studying sharks. The walls of the cage are made of a very strong metal and this stops the sharks biting the divers inside. People can take their cameras and video equipment inside the cage, and they can watch the sharks and photograph them, without any danger.

The cage also has special floats on the top, so it stays on the surface and doesn't go down too far into the water. When they are standing inside the cage, the divers can see the sharks very well, and can study how they eat and live. But the sharks can't eat them!

Rodney's idea was a good one and, today, many people use shark cages. Divers and scientists can study the sharks close up and take photographs – but they don't have to worry about shark bites. They don't have to get as close as Rodney! In this way, scientists can learn a lot more about sharks and their lives. This can help the sharks. People will not be afraid of sharks because they will understand them better.

Shark Attacks – The Facts

Many people are frightened of sharks. They read stories in the newspapers about shark attacks – like the story of Rodney Fox – and of course they watch films like *Jaws*. When they see these pictures, they see that sharks are dangerous and frightening killers – killers that like the taste of blood! So people get more and more frightened. For some people, they don't have to see a film – just the idea or thought of a shark makes them terrified!

But in fact there are not many shark attacks – and sharks are not the biggest killers of people. More people are killed by cars in car crashes, or by lightning in a storm, than by sharks. So why are we more frightened of sharks?

The word "shark" frightens many people, and they think that all sharks are dangerous. They are often very frightened of swimming in an area where there are sharks. It is a good idea to be careful – but not all sharks are killers.

Stories and films about shark attacks make people frightened.

There are more than 300 different species – or kinds – of sharks in the world. Only about 30 of these species attack humans. Sharks are beautiful, and it is good to watch them and photograph them. It is a pity to kill sharks which are not dangerous. But there are three very dangerous species: the great white shark, the bull shark, and the tiger shark.

If people are swimming in water where these three species live, they have to be very careful. These sharks are strong and fast. They can swim more quickly than human beings. They are not afraid of people. They can kill people very quickly.

A tiger shark is large and strong. It can attack most of the other living things swimming in the sea.

Bull sharks can swim almost anywhere – they can live in fresh water and sea water.

The great white shark is the most frightening and dangerous type of shark. It can attack people – and boats.

So where are these big sharks? Where is it dangerous to swim in the water? Which countries have a lot of these dangerous sharks? What kind of water do they like?

We can find sharks almost everywhere in the world, but they like warm water best. So some places are more dangerous than others, and most shark attacks are in Australia, Brazil, California, Florida, Hawaii, and South Africa.

Some people think it is safer to swim where there are a lot of people. But this is not always true – the noise of many people playing in the water can attract a shark. Sharks usually attack near beaches where lots of people go to swim and play water sports – like sailing and surfing.

Some beaches in these countries have shark signs. They warn swimmers that there are sharks in the area. People need to be careful if they go swimming off these beaches.

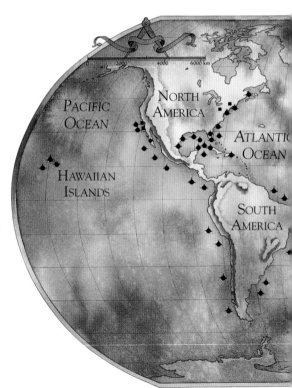

▲ This symbol shows all the places where we know sharks have attacked and killed people.

However, the number of shark attacks in a year is really quite small. In a very bad year, only 80 to 100 people are attacked in the whole world. Today, with modern, fast transport and good hospitals and doctors, only 10 to 15 of these people may die in a year. Think about how many people are killed by cars!

In fact, most sharks do not attack people who are in the water – when a shark sees someone who is swimming, it usually swims past and is not interested. So why do some sharks attack people?

This is one of the questions which scientists are studying. This is why scientists and divers follow sharks and photograph them. They want to understand them. They want to discover why the sharks attack some people, but not other people. Is it smell, or sound, or appearance that attracts a shark? Why are some sharks dangerous?

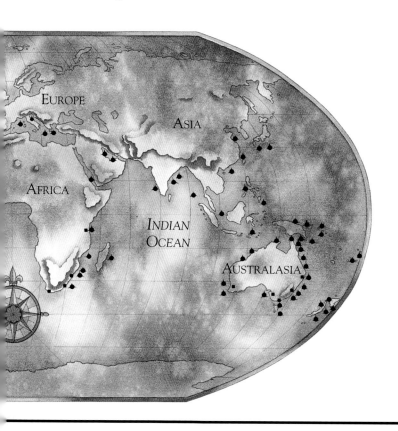

Perhaps a shark attacks because it feels frightened. A shark may have its own place or territory to look after.

Sometimes a diver does not know this, and swims into the shark's territory. In this situation, the shark may only bite the diver once, and watch him or her swim away. It only wants to look after or protect its territory.

This may explain what happened to a diver called Henry Bsource. After meeting a shark, Henry now has only one leg. A large shark took one bite and then Henry swam away – the shark didn't swim after him, and it didn't want to eat him.

Other sharks attack divers when they are fishing – like Rodney Fox. The divers kill the fish and then put the dead fish on their line. Sometimes, there is a lot of blood in the water and a lot of noise – and sharks can smell the blood and hear the noise from very far away.

When they smell the blood, the sharks know that there is something that they can eat. If they are hungry, they swim towards the blood. Noise also attracts sharks. They can hear sounds when they are a long way away. And, of course, they can swim very, very quickly towards the sound. Before a swimmer knows that there are any sharks near, the shark is there!

Henry Bource

To the shark, a seal and a surfer can look the same.

Sometimes, the shark can't see very well and it makes a mistake! For example, when a shark is swimming under the water and looks up, a surfer on a surfboard can look like a seal – and to the shark that looks very good because seals are the shark's favourite food!

But when the shark bites the surfboard, it tastes bad so the shark is not interested any more and goes away. Many surfers can tell a "shark attack" story like this – and they have the surfboard with the shark's bite to show everyone!

A bite like this is a great story … but it is very frightening when you are on the surfboard! Perhaps the shark will bite the surfboard … or perhaps it will bite your leg and perhaps you will fall off the board.

A 4–metre tiger shark bit this surfer's board in Hawaii, USA.

Of course, some sharks attack because they are very hungry – and experts think that a really hungry shark attacked Raymond Short. Raymond was swimming in the sea near a beach in Australia. He wasn't alone – there were many people on the beach and in the water. Everyone was happy and playing in the sun – they weren't thinking about sharks.

Raymond was swimming up and down near the beach when suddenly a shark bit him. Luckily, the other people on the beach saw him and heard him shouting for help. The big beaches in Australia usually have lifeguards to look after the people, and immediately lots of lifeguards ran into the water to help Raymond.

They started to carry Raymond back to the beach – but there was a problem, and Raymond felt very heavy. Suddenly they saw that the shark was still biting Raymond's leg!

The lifeguards were very surprised! What should they do? What could make the shark open its mouth? They didn't want to hurt Raymond, but they knew he was in great danger. This was a new shark problem! And they had to be quick.

The shark was now coming out of the water, and it was in danger – but it didn't open its mouth. Everyone was surprised. The shark stopped biting only when Raymond was out of the water and on the beach!

Later, the people saw that the shark was hurt – it had a big cut in its stomach. Perhaps it was hurt when it was hunting other fish before, or perhaps some fishermen hurt it.

Experts think that this shark was not able to catch its normal food, and it was very, very hungry. It had to eat something – so it tried to eat Raymond. But sharks do not usually swim into danger like this. They are intelligent creatures and they know what is dangerous and what is not.

People usually think that sharks attack in the sea. But one shark attack happened in a very strange place – a river in the USA! People don't expect to find sharks in rivers.

Lester Stilwell was 12 years old and he was swimming with his friends in the Matawan river near his home. It was a beautiful, sunny day. There were some boys in the water, and some children and adults were watching them from the river bank. No one was thinking about sharks. They were all having a good time.

Suddenly Lester shouted loudly – everyone looked round and saw his head go under the water. Lester's head didn't come back up again! Immediately one of the men on the river bank, called Stanley Fisher, jumped into the river to help Lester. He swam up to Lester and started to pull his body out of the water. Then, Stanley felt something hit his right leg very hard. "What was that?" he thought. He put his hand down to feel his leg – but there was nothing there! It was a shark attack, and sadly, both Lester and Stanley died.

Everybody was very surprised to see a shark in a river. But was this really strange? Not when you know something about sharks. Some sharks live in fresh water. They didn't find the shark that killed Lester and Stanley, but it was probably a bull shark.

Bull sharks can live in both fresh water and sea water. They can swim happily in rivers and the sea. They like to eat river fish and sea fish. Because people don't expect to see sharks in rivers, bull sharks are very, very dangerous. It is difficult to remember about the danger if it is not always there. So swimming in rivers is often more dangerous than swimming in the sea.

Sharks and Safety

How can people be safe in the water? How can we learn more about sharks – and stop shark attacks? If we understand more about sharks, then we will know how to stop the attacks.

Here are some different things people can do to protect themselves in the water. Of course, these things cost money, but many countries think this is necessary. They know that, if people are afraid of sharks, they will not come to their beaches. Their tourism industry will suffer. For many countries, the money from tourism is very important. So countries where there are a lot of sharks will invest money in research and in machinery.

One thing that stops sharks attacking is a shark net. When you put a shark net in the water, it can stop the sharks getting too close to swimmers. A shark net is like a big wall in the water and the sharks can't swim through – they can't get near the beach. Many beaches in Australia and South Africa have shark nets to protect people, and the swimmers there can feel safe. But there are problems – these nets cost a lot of money to make, and someone has to look after them all the time. They have to dive into the water to see if the net is still good, and to fix any holes. It can take a lot of time! The nets can also hurt smaller fish that get caught in them.

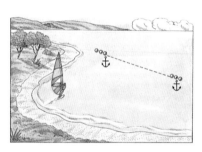

A shark net near a beach.

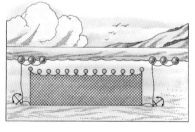

The net stops sharks swimming near the beach.

A big problem with shark nets is that they catch and kill many things, not only the dangerous sharks.

Another idea is to use electricity as a "wall", because sharks will not swim through strong electric currents. Machines send the electricity out into the water. This can be dangerous, but it works well. It is also expensive. Is it better to spend lots of money and protect the tourists? Or is it better to save the money? It is a difficult question to answer.

If you visit a place with sharks:
- Don't go in the water if you are bleeding. Sharks can smell blood more than 1.6 kilometres away.
- Don't swim in the evening because sharks like to eat at this time.
- Don't urinate in the sea because sharks can smell this (like blood) and they will come to the smell.
- Don't swim alone.
- If someone sees a shark, get out of the water.

There are also ways to protect people from sharks in an emergency. People who are in the sea after an accident – for example a plane crash or a shipwreck – are in a lot of danger. They are usually very far away from the land and sharks can see or smell them easily. And, of course, after an accident, people are often very frightened. They can panic and it is sometimes difficult for them to think clearly.

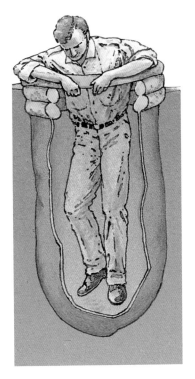

One idea to help people like this is called the shark screen bag. It is like a big plastic bag, and it is closed at the bottom. On the top of the bag, there are special floats. These keep the bag on the surface and the person's head above the water. When you are not using it, you can carry the bag easily in a pocket because it is very small. But when it is open, it is very big and a person can stand inside.

The shark can't see anyone move inside this bag – or hear or smell them. A person is safe from shark attacks inside the bag, and can wait for help.

The shark bag is very good. It is cheap to make, and easy to use. Even people in an accident, or who are hurt and bleeding, can easily use a shark bag. There are no complicated instructions. And the bag stops sharks from smelling the blood. Shark bags can save a lot of lives.

Another way to stop sharks is to use chemicals – not to kill the sharks, but to keep them away. The smell or the colour are important. The repellent must stay in the water.

Many people in the past have tried to make a chemical shark repellent to keep sharks away.

In World War II (1939–45), sharks killed many soldiers and sailors who fell into the water when their ships went down. The army tried to make a special repellent with different chemicals and dyes (colours). They wanted something to keep the sharks away, and stop the sharks seeing the soldiers. But the chemical they made wasn't very good – it disappeared into the water very quickly, and the soldiers were soon in danger again.

One new idea is to use the chemicals which are also used by another fish – the moses sole. This fish is slow, but it can stop shark attacks! Now experts think we can learn from the moses sole. The moses sole makes a very special chemical – if a shark catches it, the moses sole sends out its chemical poison. The sharks hate the taste of this poison, and they immediately drop the fish and go away.

This is a good example of how we can learn from nature. Often it is better to learn from other creatures than to use lots of chemicals. It is more efficient – and more ecological. It is better to use something that does not hurt sharks or that does not injure any of the other creatures which live in the sea.

Moses sole are slow swimmers – but they have a special poison to stop shark attacks.

Today, many people like to dive in the sea for sport, and many others want to study and film life under the water. These people may often come face to face with dangerous sharks. How do they protect themselves?

Some divers carry spear guns, or bangsticks (with a small explosive charge) to kill the sharks. But many divers want to study the sharks – not to kill them. So what can they do?

This is often a difficult question for people who like creatures. They do not want to hurt the creatures, but they want to go near to them. If a person goes very near a creature, it can become afraid. When a creature is afraid, it often attacks.

A bangstick can kill a large shark immediately.

Two Australian film makers called Valerie and Ron Taylor had a new idea to protect divers. In their job they had to take photographs under the water but it was dangerous work. Valerie knows this – she can show you her shark bites! They needed something to protect them from the sharks.

One day, the Taylors saw something interesting on their ship – a fisherman was cleaning some fish and he was wearing a pair of very strange gloves. "What are they?" Valerie asked the fisherman. "Can I see them?"

Valerie and Ron looked at the fisherman's gloves very carefully, and asked the man many questions. The gloves were made from stainless steel, and they protected the man's hands very well. This gave the Taylors an idea.

"This is what we are looking for! But we don't want just gloves, we want a whole suit, like the suits the soldiers wore a long time ago!" they thought.

Valerie and Ron looked at pictures of soldiers in the Middle Ages. The soldiers wore metal suits, and metal gloves on their hands, and metal helmets on their heads. The metal suits were usually made of iron. They were very heavy, but they protected the soldiers very well.

Valerie and Ron decided to use stainless steel for their special suit. Stainless steel is much lighter than iron, so the Taylors made a suit with 400,000 very small stainless steel rings.

When the suit was finished, it looked good. But was it good enough to stop a shark? They had to test it.

Who would be brave enough to wear the suit in the water?

Shark suits
Small rings on a shark suit stop the shark's teeth, so the shark can't bite through the person's skin. But it will still hurt.

Valerie in her chain-mail suit.

Valerie was the brave person! "OK, I'll do it!" she said.

Ron and Valerie travelled to a place near California to test the suit. They knew there were a lot of sharks there. They chose a beach which was very quiet. The water was warm, and very clear. It was ideal for filming … and for sharks! They decided to test the suit there.

First, Valerie put on her normal diving suit, then Ron helped her to put on the new shark suit. It took a long time. It was difficult to put one suit over the other.

When she was ready, they threw some pieces of fish into the water for the sharks. Valerie went into the water, and they both waited.

After a few minutes, they saw the first sharks. They were interested in the fish – not in Valerie. They swam up to it and began to eat it. Valerie watched. Then she had an idea.

She took a bleeding fish in her hand. The blood was making the sea red. She waited. Very quickly, a shark smelt the blood. It came nearer and nearer. Suddenly it was very near Valerie, and it bit her arm. She was surprised and a little frightened, but she was OK!

Then the other sharks came nearer – and this time they did not stop. They were all around her! They bit Valerie again and again – all over her body. On the boat, the others were watching and worrying. There were so many sharks in the water, and they couldn't see Valerie! In the water, Valerie was frightened, but she was happy. The sharks' teeth couldn't bite through the stainless steel. The suit was good!

"I was a bit frightened at times," said Valerie later. "One shark pulled my glove off, and then it bit my thumb! It was very strong, and it was hungry. But I was lucky. The suit was great! But I was very happy to swim up to the surface, and to get away!"

Ron Taylor listened carefully to Valerie. They discussed the experiment. Valerie described what the sharks did when they touched the suit. Then they went back to work. The suit was good – but they wanted to make it better. They had to make some small changes and then it was perfect. Thanks to Valerie Taylor, we had the first shark suit.

A diver wearing a shark suit to stop sharks biting.

About Sharks

Sharks have been here in the world for a very long time. There were sharks in the seas nearly 400 million years ago, and they are 200 million years older than the dinosaurs. We know that they have been here a long time, but the sharks we see in the water today are very like those first sharks millions of years ago.

If we study sharks today, we can learn more about these ancient creatures. We can also learn more about the sea and the sea-bed. If we learn about these things, we can understand better how the earth changes. Some things are very different from how they were long ago, but some things are nearly the same. If we can understand the present and the past, perhaps we can guess about the future!

People think that sharks today are frightening, but some of the first sharks were very, very big! These sharks were much more frightening than the sharks we can see today!

The biggest of these early sharks was called *Carcharodon megalodon*. This shark had a huge mouth – its enormous jaws were more than 1.8 metres wide – and it was 16 metres long. That is twice as long as today's great white shark. And *Carcharodon megalodon* was very, very heavy. It weighed up to 4,535 kilograms.

Frightening fossils
Millions of years ago, when sharks died, they fell to the bottom of the sea and into the sand. Now we can find their fossils – and sometimes we can find fossils of the hard parts like the teeth and bones.

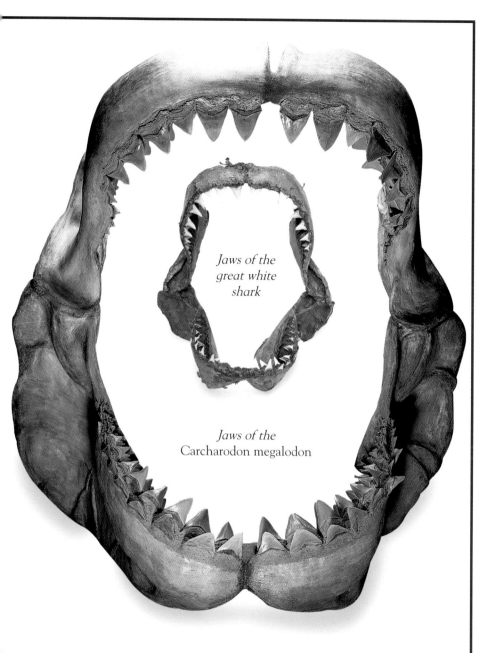

*Jaws of the
great white
shark*

Jaws of the
Carcharodon megalodon

Now there are no more of these big sharks – they are extinct. But we can still learn something about them. Life in the sea today is very like it was a long time ago. So we can study sharks today and, at the same time, learn about life millions of years ago.

After millions of years in the water, the shark is now the perfect underwater hunter. Its streamlined body is made of cartilage – the same as our noses and ears – instead of bones. This means that it can bend and move more easily in the water.

Sharks have the same five senses as people. A shark can see, hear, smell, taste, and touch. But the shark has more senses as well! It has two more senses for hunting creatures underwater – and they are very strange.

One of the shark's "extra" senses is for feeling vibrations in the water. The other extra sense is for detecting living things. These two special senses help the shark to find things to eat. They are very important, and make the shark a very efficient underwater creature! Let's look at these two senses in more detail.

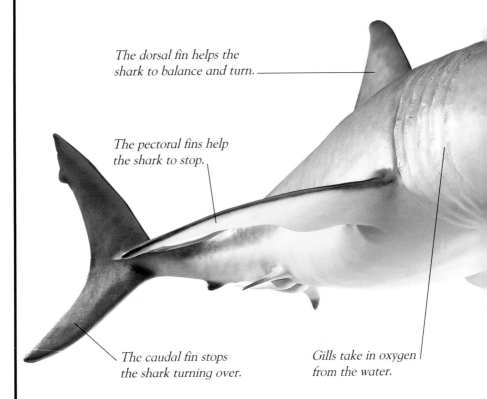

The dorsal fin helps the shark to balance and turn.

The pectoral fins help the shark to stop.

The caudal fin stops the shark turning over.

Gills take in oxygen from the water.

Sharks often find their food from a distance. They can sense vibrations in the water, so they know that something is moving. The sixth sense helps them to do this. It is on a shark's body. Down each side of the shark's body, you can find a line of special points under the skin called a "lateral line". The shark uses these points to feel small vibrations or movements in the water.

Of course, some moving things are not good enough to eat! A shark wants to know if the object is just a plant, or a piece of wood, or if it is alive. The seventh sense helps with this. This sense is on the shark's head. There are very small holes on the shark's head called the "ampullae of Lorenzini". The shark uses these holes to feel the small electrical charges from all living things.

These senses help the shark to be the perfect hunter.

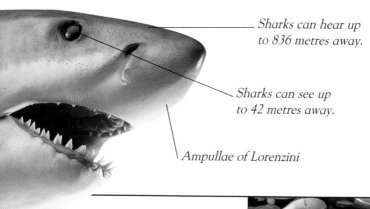

Sharks can hear up to 836 metres away.

Sharks can see up to 42 metres away.

Ampullae of Lorenzini

Shark skin
A shark's skin has very small scales (like teeth). People used shark's skin in the past as a tool to make wood smooth.

Today, we know a little about sharks, but not very much! Sharks are mysterious creatures. They are different from many other creatures. For example, many shark species do not live in groups – they like to live, swim, and hunt alone. Perhaps this is more efficient.

The blue shark is different. It lives in very big groups – up to one thousand blue sharks sometimes live in a group.

Experts know very little about the life of a shark, but they do know that sharks are very slow to reproduce (have babies). In fact, some sharks are 11 years old before they reproduce. When they do reproduce, they don't have many babies. This means that these sharks are able to look after their young very well.

Many sharks lay eggs like other fish, and they put their eggs in strong bags, called egg cases, to protect them (*see the picture below*). The eggs are safe inside the cases. Other creatures cannot eat them. They can grow bigger inside the cases.

Other sharks do not lay eggs, they have live babies called pups. But the sea is a very dangerous place for small pups, and so when they are born, shark pups are quite big. This makes it more difficult for other creatures to attack the pups because they are big enough to defend themselves.

Egg cases

Shark pups

Sharks like to eat, and they eat many different kinds of food – all sharks eat fish and meat and the things in the sea. Many sharks eat small fish and animals like lobsters and jellyfish.

Basking shark

But sharks eat other things in the sea, too. This can cause problems. They eat the rubbish we throw into the sea – like tin cans and plastic bags. Eating rubbish is very dangerous for the sharks. If a shark eats a plastic bag, it can choke. It cannot breathe properly. Tin cans can hurt a shark's mouth, and its insides. So human pollution is bad for sharks.

Some sharks eat bigger animals like seals, penguins – and other sharks. They use their sharp teeth and their strong muscles to catch their prey. They are good hunters!

But not all sharks are hunters. Some species, like the basking shark, don't hunt anything at all – they just swim along through the water with their mouths wide open! These sharks eat plankton (the very small plant and animal life in the sea) and also small animals like shrimps. It is strange that a big creature like a shark can live on such very small creatures.

Jellyfish

Seals

37

Do you think you know what a shark looks like? Close your eyes and think of a shark – what do you see? Now look at these pictures – and perhaps you will think again!

When most people think of sharks, they think of the great white shark. This is the shark we see in stories and films. But not all sharks look like the great white. You can see sharks in all sizes – and some of them look very strange!

The hammerhead shark uses the detectors on the side of its head to find food. It moves its head from side to side while it swims. It can "sense" the movement of other creatures.

The biggest shark is the whale shark. It can grow up to 12.2 metres long and it can weigh up to 13.2 tonnes. The whale shark is the largest fish in the world today.

Hammerhead shark

Lantern shark

Angel shark

The smallest shark species in the world is called a lantern shark. The lantern shark is very small for a shark. It only grows to be 20 centimetres long. It gets its name, the lantern shark, because its eyes light up in the dark – just like a lantern or light.

There are many other species of sharks in the sea. Each one is different from the others. For example, the thresher shark has a long, thin tail. It beats the water with its tail when it is hunting. Scientists think that the thresher shark also hits fish on the head with its tail, so they become unconscious.

Look at the different shark species shown on these pages. You can see why scientists and ordinary people are so interested in sharks! They are all so different!

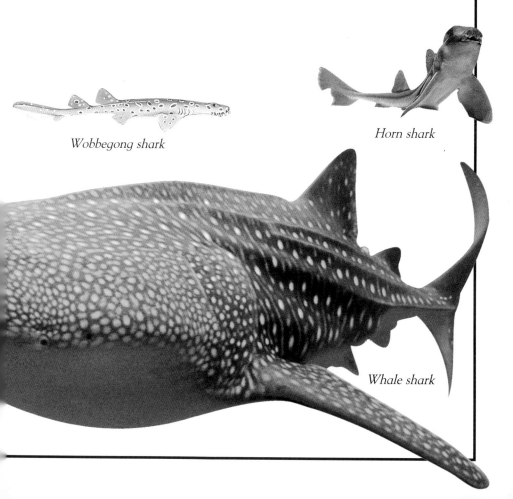

Wobbegong shark

Horn shark

Whale shark

Shark Attack or People Attack?

Everyone talks about shark attacks, and people say they are frightened of sharks. But, today, people are more dangerous than sharks. How do people attack sharks?

Shark's tooth necklace

One big problem is overfishing – that is when people catch too many fish. Because of overfishing, the number of some species of fish is very small – soon they may be extinct (just like the *Carcharodon megalodon*). If there are not enough fish, the sharks cannot find enough food.

People have tried to hunt and catch sharks for many years. In the past, fishermen caught the sharks and ate the meat. It was a cheap food for fishermen and their families, and they sold it in the markets for money.

However, the shark was more than just food – the people made weapons and jewellery with the sharks' teeth. But they were careful, and they only took the fish they needed. They only caught a few sharks, and so the number of sharks in the sea was never a problem.

Today, fishing has changed. People have modern equipment and fishing boats, and they can catch a lot of sharks – up to 100 million every year! Now the number of some types of sharks is down – sometimes by about 80% in the last 10 years. Some experts are very worried about the future for sharks. They think that some species can disappear. If there is no food for them, and if bigger and bigger boats chase them, it is difficult for them to survive.

But sharks have other problems, too. They often get caught in fishing nets, and they can't get away. When they pull up their nets, the fishermen take all the fish they want and throw the other fish (like sharks) back into the sea – dead. These sharks are killed for nothing.

Some people like to hunt and kill sharks for sport. They think that they look very brave and clever when they catch and kill a shark, and it makes a very good photograph to show their friends. But these people are never in any real danger – only the shark is in danger. After the kill, they can put the shark's jaws on their wall to show friends – or they sell the jaws to tourists.

Killing sharks is not a fair sport. The people often have lots of modern equipment. They use radio to find the sharks. They do not fight the sharks in the same way as the fishermen. They do not do it for food, but for fun.

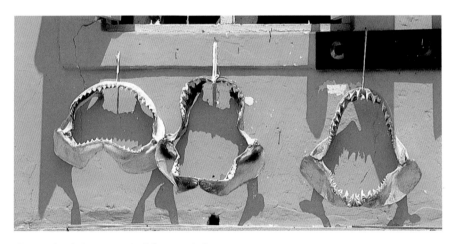

Some sharks' jaws on a fisherman's boat.

Shark meal

Sharks are also in danger because, in many parts of the world, people like to eat shark meat. In some countries, shark meat is very special. In Asia, for example, shark-fin soup is a very expensive meal. Fishermen can get a lot of money for shark fins in these countries. So what do they do? They catch the shark, cut off the fin, and throw the rest of the shark's body back into the water to die. These fishermen are not interested in the shark meat, or the shark. They are only interested in the money they get for the fins. Some organizations try to educate the fishermen to use the whole shark. But the fishermen say it costs too much to sell the ordinary shark meat.

You can use fins from any type of shark to make shark-fin soup.

In some countries, shark cartilage is also very important – it is made into health pills or medicine. People think that if they take these pills made from sharks, they will feel better – even from serious illnesses like heart disease or cancer. Usually, these stories are not true. But, in many countries, people like to use traditional medicines like these. Their grandparents used them, and they believe they are better than modern medicines.

Sharks are also killed for clothes. The shark's skin is used to make expensive leather belts for skirts and trousers, and wallets to keep money in. Many people do not wear fur coats from animals now. They think it is like wearing a dead animal. But they do not think about shark's skin in the same way.

A box made from shark leather.

People kill sharks for other things, too. When we think about sharks, we usually think about the teeth or the fin, but one of the most important parts of the shark is its liver. The oil from a shark's liver is used to make many things – like oils for industry, for example, and medicines. In the past, people used shark oil to make vitamin A pills – it was the most important way to get this vitamin. But luckily, in the 1950s, they started to find vitamin A in other places, so they stopped using the sharks.

Vitamin A tablets

Cruel creams
The liver and other parts of the shark are used to make beauty creams – but it is possible to stop using the sharks and to use the oil from plants.

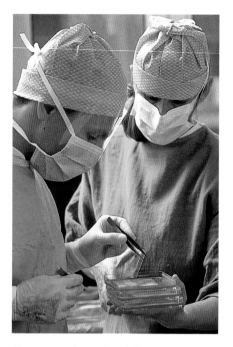
Doctors with artificial skin grown from shark cartilage.

If we don't stop killing all these sharks, soon there may be no more sharks left in the sea – they will be extinct. "But do we want to have sharks?" some people ask. "They are dangerous. They are a problem for swimmers. They are a problem for the tourist industry. They can attack fishermen."

However, many other people think we do need to have a lot of sharks and we must do what we can to protect them. They are beautiful, they can give us a lot of things (if we don't kill them all), and there are many things we have been able to learn from sharks.

Some of these things are very surprising. The sharks can help us to understand the sea, and other creatures. Perhaps we can learn many more things from sharks in the future.

For example, some medical experts already think that sharks may be able to help us to stop cancer – one of the most serious illnesses today. These experts have discovered that squaline – a special chemical made in the liver and stomach of the dogfish shark – can slow down the growth of cancer in a person's brain.

The cartilage of the shark is also very useful, because it is very strong. Doctors are able to use cartilage from the shark to make new skin for people who have been burnt in a fire. So the shark can be useful for medicine in another way.

Perhaps sharks can also help people who have a lot of cuts – like in a car accident. They have very strong immune systems – that means they are very healthy, and they don't usually feel ill. The shark's immune system can fight illness very well and when a shark is cut, the cut gets better very quickly. Sharks don't usually get cancer like other animals – even when doctors put cancer cells into their bodies.

Why are they so healthy? The experts don't know the answer yet. But if we can study the sharks, perhaps we can help more people who are ill.

So sharks are not only useful for food and clothes and medicine. They can teach us how to live better, and they can help us fight modern diseases.

It is easy to think of sharks as dangerous animals. Of course, they *are* dangerous, and we must never forget this, but perhaps we can learn to understand them, and to use them without killing too many of them.

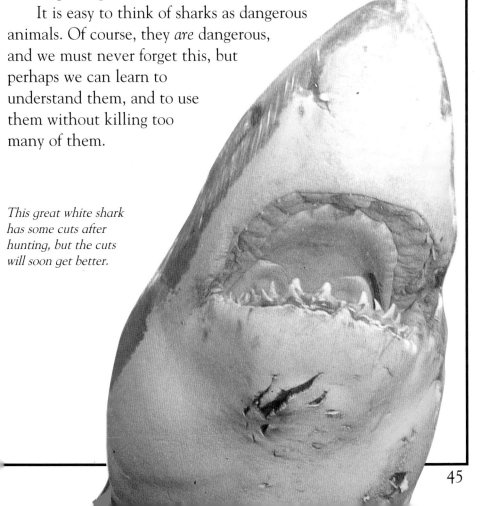

This great white shark has some cuts after hunting, but the cuts will soon get better.

One good place to go and see a shark is an aquarium, and there are no shark attacks!

The more we learn about sharks, the more surprised and interested we are. Of course, many people are still afraid of sharks and shark attacks. They don't want to come face to face with a great white shark, like Rodney Fox! But everyone can learn about sharks today – it is not always dangerous.

How can we learn more about them? We can visit sharks in aquariums to see them close up. Go to your local zoo or aquarium. Ask about the sharks. Spend a long time looking at them. See how they move. You will begin to see the differences between the different species.

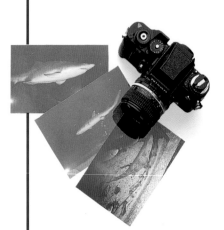

We can also watch the beautiful films of sharks made by underwater photographers like Valerie and Ron Taylor.

Or, if we are brave, we can dive with experts to see the sharks in the sea.

Sharks are beautiful, surprising, and intelligent – and only a few shark species are dangerous. A very small number of people are attacked by sharks every year – so sharks are not really the frightening killers we see in stories and films – killers with a taste for blood.

We hope this book will make you think about sharks, and realize what wonderful creatures they are. There are lots more shark stories – sad ones and funny ones. But most of them are exciting. However, remember the surprising things about sharks too. There are lots more things to discover. There are so many things we can learn from studying sharks.

Sharks have lived in this world for a very long time – millions of years longer than people have been on the earth. Will they continue to live here with us – or will people finally kill them all?

Glossary

Ampullae of Lorenzini
Tiny holes on a shark's head that can feel electrical signals in the water.

aquarium
A large container where fish and sea animals are kept so that people can look at them safely.

bangstick
A special gun used under the water. It can kill a shark.

Carcharodon megalodon
The largest shark that ever lived in the sea. The last one died over 10 million years ago.

cartilage
The strong material that makes a shark's skeleton. Human noses and ears are also made of cartilage.

cancer
A very serious disease where cells in one part of the body start to grow in a strange way.

extinct
When all of a particular species of animal or plant die, and there are none left on Earth.

fins
Parts of a fish that stick out from its body. (See picture of shark's fins page 34.)

fossils
Parts of a plant or animal that lived millions of years ago. Often found in rocks.

immune system
The system in your body that stops you getting ill.

lateral line
A line of points along each side of a shark's body that helps the shark to feel movements in the water.

plankton
Very tiny animals that live in the sea.

shark cage
A special metal box that protects divers under the water.

shark net
A net that is put under the water to stop sharks swimming near the people on a beach.

shark screen bag
A special plastic bag that protects people in the water. The sharks cannot see the people move or smell them.

shrimps
Small, pink seafood with a soft shell.

spear gun
An underwater gun that fires spears (see page 5). Some divers use this to catch fish.

squaline
An important chemical in a shark's liver. Humans use it for medicine.